The Great Bookworm

Kristina Murray-Hally
Illustrated by Hanlik Arts

To our beautiful Bookworms who GLOW!
May you continue to 'consume & share'
knowledge and in doing so you'll LIGHT
UP the WORLD!

First published in Australia by
Spiders 8 Media
Postal: PO BOX 2379 Ivanhoe East Vic 3079
Email: murrayhally@gmail.com
Website: www.kristinamurray-hally.com

National Library of Australia Cataloguing-in-Publication entry
Creator: Murray-Hally, Kristina, author.
Title: The great bookworm / Kristina Murray-Hally ;
Illustrated by Hanlik Arts.
ISBN: 9780994273833 (paperback)
Target Audience: For children
Subjects: Book-worms--Juvenile fiction.
Learning--Juvenile fiction.
Children's stories.

Cover design by graphic designer
Hanlik Arts

Printed in Australia

One cool, spring morning Albi shot up through a mound of dirt.

"Where am I?" he said surveying the area, when a group of worms appeared out of nowhere.

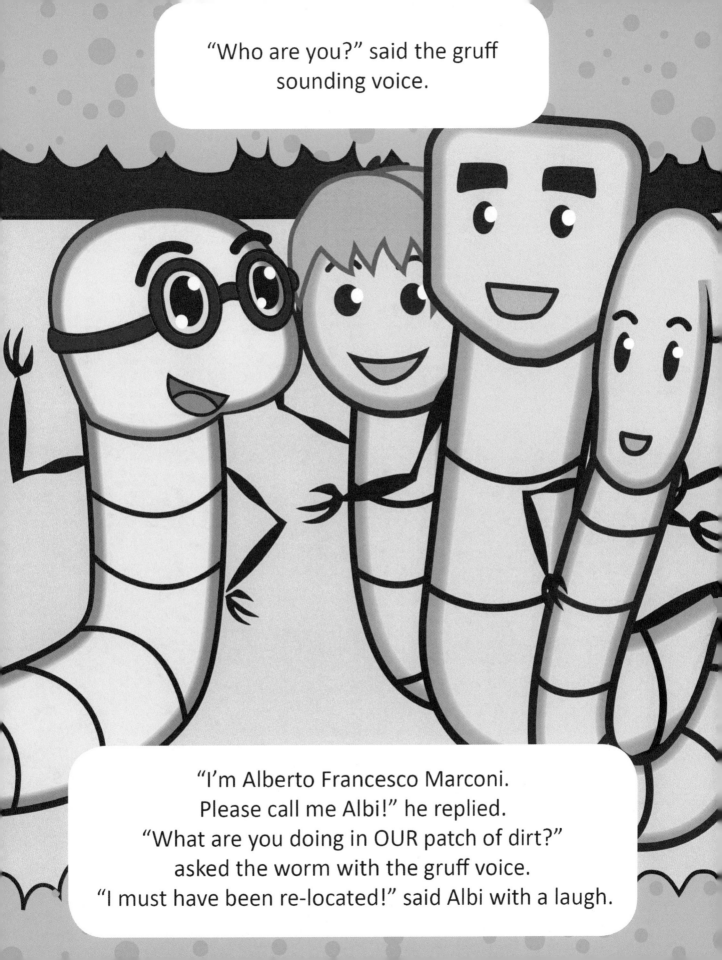

After breakfast Albi set off to have a better look at his new environment.

Over the next month he grew bigger, healthier and happier – there was a glow about him! All the other worms began to notice and started to feel jealous.

Junior Fiction

"Why are you so happy?" asked the Gruff Worm.

"For lunch I visited the library and chewed through all the children's picture books!" Albi replied.

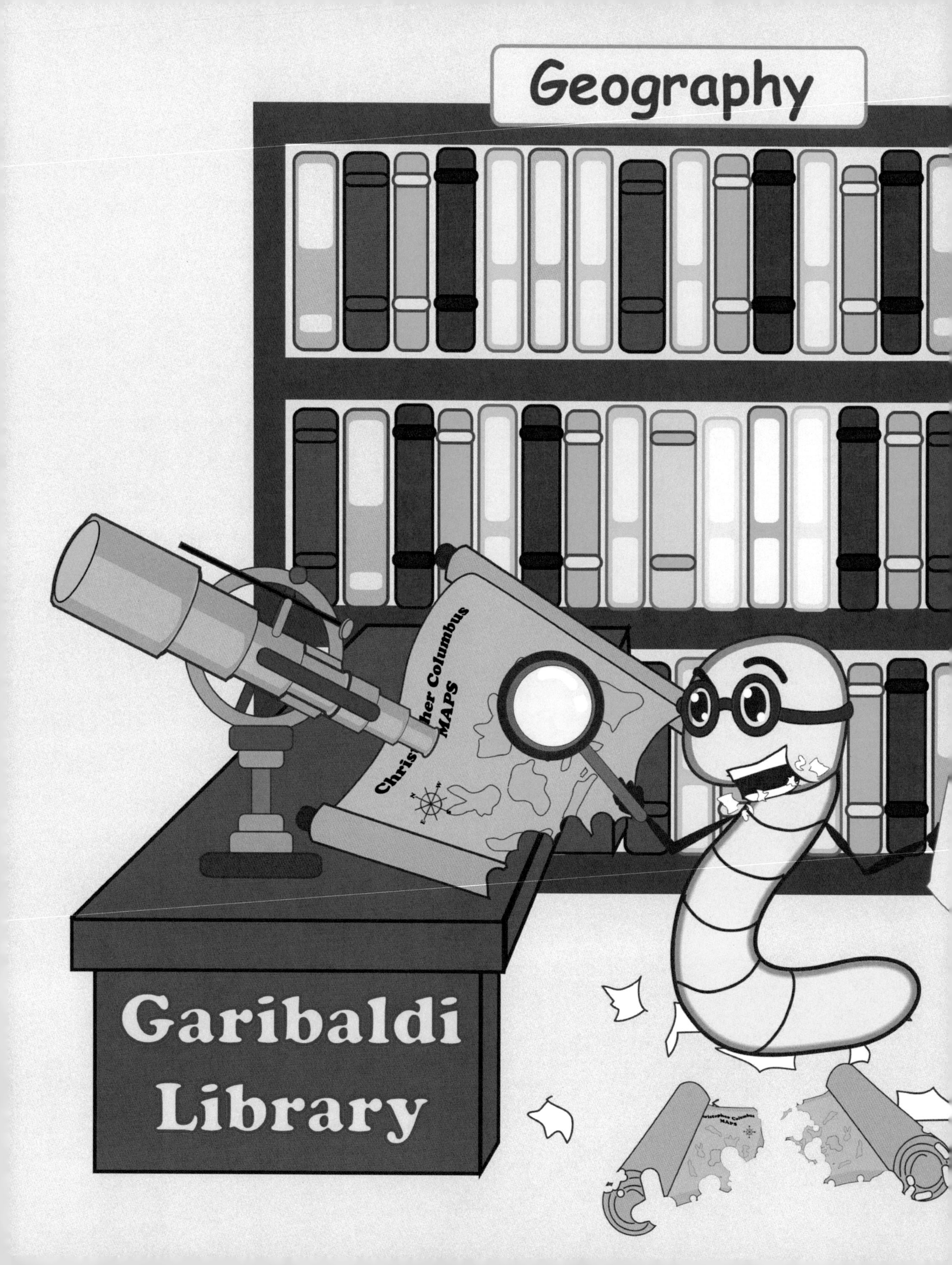

Geography
Christopher Columbus
MAPS
Garibaldi
Library

With that the Gruff Worm and his friends slid off to the library before closing time.

The next morning Gruff Worm asked Albi, "Are you planning to go to the library sometime today? We were thinking we could join you!"

"Sorry," said Albi, "I'm staying at home to reflect and digest the information."
"Reflecting and digesting!" repeated the Gruff Worm, puzzled, as he slithered off.

"How did you go?" the worms asked Gruff Worm.
"No luck. He's reflecting and digesting!"
All the worms found this very amusing, and were
bent over laughing hysterically.

"So I hear you would like to know my secret to success?" Albi said, smirking at Gruff Worm and his friends.

"Only if you have time," Gruff Worm said in a sweet voice.

"Meet me out the front of the library under the large shady tree at 10.00am tomorrow," said Albi.

"Good morning and welcome to The Worm School," said Albi. "The Worm School is all about the love of learning, and where you will eat many, many words and where you will inhale many, many ideas! You will also wriggle across many, many images and then return home to think about how you can use the knowledge," Albi explained.

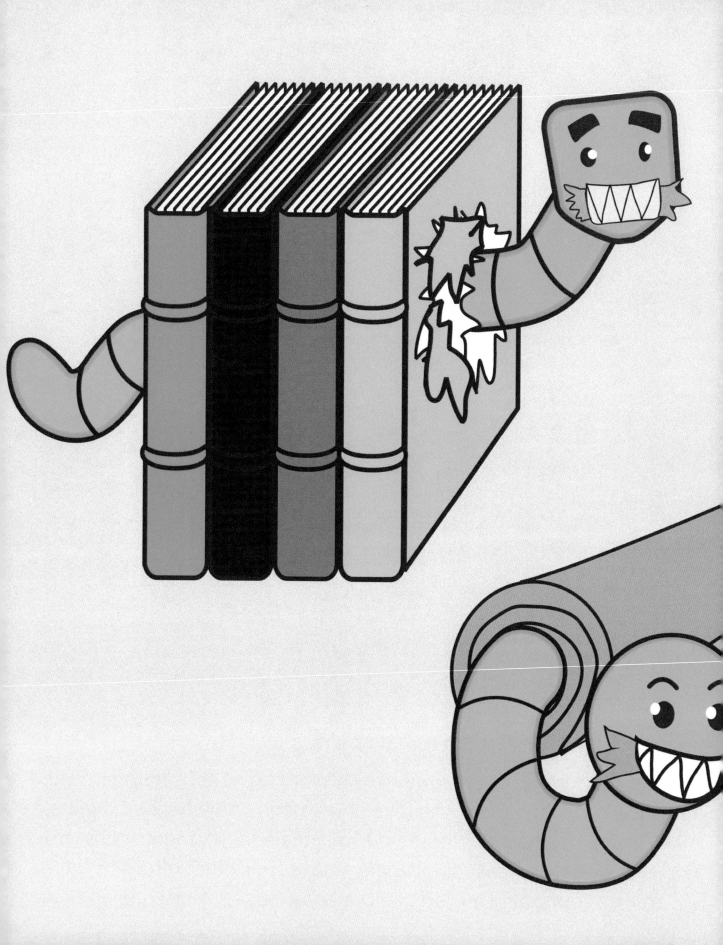

Today's lesson is about speed reading. There are over 120 million items in the Garibaldi Library so speed reading is crucial!

Acknowledgements

The Great Bookworm was truly inspired by my love of books, learning and visiting libraries, museums and art galleries. This book, like my other creations, has been a result of a great amount of work and my wonderful team.

Many thanks go to Hanlik Arts for his fantastic designs and amazing artwork. He is a great artist, fabulous to work with and crucial in the creation of this book.

It is with much gratitude that we say thank you to Willy Tanuwijaya for his wonderful work with the typesetting and layout of this book. Willy and Hanlik Arts are a fabulous team and are an absolute pleasure and an honour to work with.

Another grand thank you to Amanda Spedding for her great editing and proofreading skills, her dedication and timely work, attention to detail, ideas and feedback.

An enormous thank you goes to our beautiful daughters, Theadora and Seraphina, my true inspiration.

Also a gigantic thank you goes to my husband, Tony, for his generosity, support and assistance in the creation of my books and writing career.

To my gorgeous parents, Rosanna and Michael, for their unconditional love, generosity, support and belief and so much more!

To family and friends for their love, encouragement and sharing in my joy.

To the children and staff at the schools and kindergartens I visit, it is a privilege to read and share with you my stories and writing journey. I love answering all of your questions and discussing the learning activities. It's so much fun and an absolute joy!

To one and all THANK YOU.

About the Author

Kristina is a children's book author who is passionate about children's literacy and education.

Kristina holds a Diploma of Teaching (Primary), Bachelor of Education (Primary) and a Masters of Education (Teaching English to Speakers of Other Languages). She enjoys being around people especially children, and listening to their stories.

She lives in Melbourne Australia with her husband Tony and daughters, Theadora and Seraphina. Kristina has always loved to write and spends many hours writing, reading, watching and listening for ideas. She carries a small notebook and pen with her to 'catch' ideas before they evaporate. Her wonderful ideas can come from anywhere at any time!

Other books by
Kristina Murray-Hally
- - - - - - - - - - - - - - - -
Max's Magnificent Glasses
Captain Loose Tooth
The Very Long Sausage Dog

Made in the USA
Middletown, DE
09 October 2020